It's another Quality Book from CGP

This book is for Key Stage Two pupils taking their Maths SATs
in May 2016 and beyond. It's packed with challenging arithmetic
questions designed to help fully prepare them for the Year 6 tests.

It also includes self-assessment tick boxes so that children
can make a note of how confident they feel about each topic
— ideal for keeping track of their progress.

What CGP is all about

Our sole aim here at CGP is to produce the highest quality books
— carefully written, immaculately presented and
dangerously close to being funny.

Then we work our socks off to get them out to you
— at the cheapest possible prices.

Contents

Published by CGP

Editors

Ceara Hayden, Kirstie McHale

With thanks to Sharon Keeley-Holden, Maxine Petrie and Lucy Towle for the proofreading.
With thanks to Judy Hornigold, Alison Griffin, Nicola Paddock and Tina Ramsden for the reviewing.

ISBN: 978 1 78294 230 6

Clipart from Corel®
Printed by Elanders Ltd, Newcastle upon Tyne.
Based on the classic CGP style created by Richard Parsons.

Written Addition

Mental Maths Warm Up

Answer these as quickly as you can, saying your answer out loud or in your head...

1. Think of 5 pairs of numbers that add to 10.
2. Say the value of each digit in the number 12345.
3. Work out 17 + 5 in your head.
4. Work out 3 + 4 + 5 in your head.

Answers: 1) E.g. 1+9, 2+8, 3+7, 4+6, 5+5 **2)** one ten thousand, two thousands, three hundreds, four tens, five units **3)** 22 **4)** 12

Now try these. Do your working in the spaces, and copy your answers into the boxes.
One has been done for you.

1 21 + 34

$$\begin{array}{r} 2\,1 \\ +\ 3\,4 \\ \hline 5\,5 \\ \hline \end{array}$$

55

2 15 + 64

3 38 + 45

4 73 + 87

5 94 + 38

6 134 + 451

7 208 + 512

8 337 + 228

Written Addition

9   791 + 148

10   652 + 547

11   484 + 267

12   227 + 583

13   953 + 787

14   2134 + 3421

15   54 + 210

Make sure you line up the digits in columns carefully!

16   94 + 701

17   942 + 30

18   7787 + 999

You could do 7787 + 1000 − 1 if you find it easier.

Written Addition

19 202 + 8798

23 222 + 33 + 44

Adding three numbers works just the same as adding two numbers together.

20 27350 + 34201

24 207 + 304 + 442

21 86425 + 57386

25 1422 + 337 + 61

22 27287 + 3443

26 88888 + 777 + 4444

A Calcugator can add up numbers with more than 4 digits in columns. Can you? Tick the box.

Written Subtraction

Answer these as quickly as you can, saying your answer out loud or in your head...

1. How many tens are there in 683?
2. What is 8 – 3?
3. Take away 5 from 27.
4. Take 20 away from 60.

Answers: 1) 8 2) 5 3) 22 4) 40

Now try these. Do your working in the spaces, and copy your answers into the boxes. One has been done for you.

1 47 – 24

```
  4 7
-  2 4
  ───
  2 3
```

23

2 58 – 26

3 95 – 13

4 64 – 26

You'll have to exchange a ten for 10 units to answer this one.

5 867 – 146

6 749 – 238

7 841 – 340

8 267 – 149

Written Subtraction

9 694 – 258

You could check your answers by adding.

14 798 – 37

10 280 – 176

15 584 – 36

11 661 – 380

16 997 – 968

12 70 – 8

17 834 – 762

13 329 – 15

Make sure you line up the hundreds, tens and units.

18 942 – 857

Written Subtraction

It can help to line up the units when you subtract numbers with different numbers of digits.

19 6485 – 3261

23 2648 – 649

You could do 2648 – 648 – 1 if you find it easier.

20 7354 – 5426

24 3344 – 444

21 5843 – 217

25 6271 – 349

22 3251 – 198

26 9064 – 318

Written Subtraction

27 82578 – 2210

31 59846 – 9000 – 34

Do 59846 – 9000 first, and then take away 34.

28 68545 – 68

32 25498 – 5586 – 12

29 45876 – 6863

33 19861 – 234 – 67

30 25186 – 6446

34 76519 – 2056 – 35

Calcugators love subtracting numbers in columns. They do it all the time. How did you do?

Section 1 — Whole Numbers

Multiplying by 10, 100 and 1000

Mental Maths Warm Up

Answer these as quickly as you can, saying your answer out loud or in your head...

1. 16 multiplied by what gives you 1600?

2. Find the missing number. 568 × ? = 5680

3. There are 1000 times more flowers in a field in Spring than in Winter.

   If there are 47 in Winter, how many are there in Spring?

Answers: 1) 100 2) 10 3) 47000

Now try these questions. Put your answers in the boxes.

1   13 × 10

To multiply by 10 move the digits one place to the left.

2   59 × 100

3   873 × 10

4   6437 × 100

5   761 × 1000

6   9530 × 10

7   4005 × 1000

8   910 × 1000

Calcugators remember to move the digits to the left when multiplying by 10, 100 and 1000. Did you?

Dividing by 10, 100 and 1000

> **Mental Maths Warm Up**
>
> *Answer these as quickly as you can, saying your answer out loud or in your head...*
>
> 1. What should you divide 30 by to get 3?
> 2. 32000 divided by what gives you 32?
> 3. What is 900 ÷ 100?
> 4. Find the missing number. 600 ÷ ? = 60
>
> Answers: 1) 10 2) 1000 3) 9 4) 10

Now try these questions. Put your answers in the boxes.

1　70 ÷ 10

To divide by 10 move the digits one place to the right.

5　74000 ÷ 100

2　550 ÷ 10

6　3000 ÷ 1000

3　9800 ÷ 100

7　68000 ÷ 1000

4　1600 ÷ 10

8　40000 ÷ 1000

If you like moving digits to the right like Calcugators, then you'll find this page ok. How do you feel?

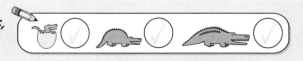

Using Times Tables

┌─ Mental Maths Warm Up ─────────────────────────────────────┐

Answer these as quickly as you can, saying your answer out loud or in your head...

1. Say the 4 times table up to 5 × 4 out loud.

2. 12 × 7 = 84. What is 13 × 7?

3. 15 × 6 = 90. What is 6 × 15?

4. Is 35 in the 8 times table?

Answers: 1) 1 × 4 = 4, 2 × 4 = 8, 3 × 4 = 12, 4 × 4 = 16, 5 × 4 = 20
2) 91 **3)** 90 **4)** No

└───┘

Now try these. Put your answers in the boxes.

1 3 × 11

5 5 × 7

5 × 7 is the same as 7 × 5

2 2 × 12

6 6 × 8

3 5 × 9

7 9 × 3

4 11 × 10

8 12 × 12

Using Times Tables

Now try using your times tables to divide.

9 12 ÷ 6

10 24 ÷ 2

11 18 ÷ 6

12 55 ÷ 5

13 28 ÷ 7

14 56 ÷ 7

15 72 ÷ 8

16 108 ÷ 12

Are you a whizz at your times tables, just like a Calcugator? Tick the box to show how you did.

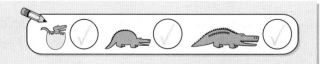

Section 1 — Whole Numbers

Multiples and Factors

Now try Questions 1 to 4. Write down the first five multiples of each number.

For Questions 5 and 6, find all the factors of each number.

1   7

5   24

2   25

3   80

6   63

4   36

Short Multiplication

Mental Maths Warm Up

Answer these as quickly as you can, saying your answer out loud or in your head...

1. Find the missing number. 18 × 5 = 5 × ?
2. What is 7 × 3?
3. What is 50 × 3?
4. Work out 57 × 3.

Answers: 1) 18 2) 21 3) 150 4) 171

Now try these. Do your working in the spaces, and copy your answers into the boxes.
One has been done for you.

1 37 × 6

```
    3 7
×     6
---------
  2 2 2
    4
```

222

2 52 × 8

3 18 × 7

4 76 × 3

5 85 × 4

6 439 × 9

Short Multiplication

7 5115 × 5

8 1495 × 3

9 1986 × 4

10 4275 × 2

11 8495 × 4

12 3196 × 9

13 2014 × 7

14 2035 × 8

Calcugators love writing out multiplications in columns. How about you? Tick the box.

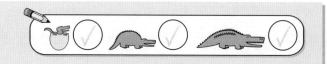

Long Multiplication

Mental Maths Warm Up

Answer these as quickly as you can, saying your answer out loud or in your head...

1. Harry buys 19 stickers for 12 friends. Estimate how many stickers he buys.
2. Estimate the answer to 399 × 19.
3. Partition the number 19 to make it easier to multiply by.
4. What is 400 × 30?

Answers: 1) E.g. 200 (20 × 10) **2)** E.g. 8000 (400 × 20) **3)** 1 ten and 9 units **4)** 12000

Now try these. Do your working in the spaces, and copy your answers into the boxes.
One has been done for you.

1
```
    2 4 7
  ×   1 8
  -------
  1 9 7 6
    3 5
  2 4 7 0
  -------
  4 4 4 6
    1 1
```

Make sure you show your working for these 2 mark questions.

4446

3
```
    6 8 5
  ×   7 1
```

2
```
    2 8 4
  ×   2 3
```

4
```
    7 6 8
  ×   3 2
```

16

Long Multiplication

5
```
    5856
×     36
_____
```

8
```
    7842
×     68
_____
```

6
```
    1955
×     54
_____
```

9
```
    4444
×     44
_____
```

Use estimating to check your answer.

7
```
    3296
×     22
_____
```

10
```
    8888
×     88
_____
```

A Calcugator enjoys using long multiplication to find the right answer. How did you find these pages?

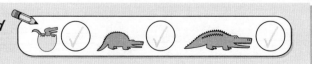

Section 1 — Whole Numbers

© CGP — not to be photocopied

Short Division with No Remainders

> Mental Maths Warm Up

Answer these as quickly as you can, saying your answer out loud or in your head...

1. Partition 245 into hundreds, tens and units.

2. What's 400 divided by 4?

3. Alan has 240 books. He divides them equally between three shelves. How many books does he have on each shelf?

4. What is 540 ÷ 9?

Now try these. Do your working in the spaces, and copy your answers into the boxes.
One has been done for you.

1 156 ÷ 4

$$4 \overline{)1\,^{15}5\,^{3}6}$$
$$3\ \ 9$$

39

2 108 ÷ 6

3 207 ÷ 9

4 448 ÷ 7

5 352 ÷ 4

6 728 ÷ 7

7 696 ÷ 8

8 495 ÷ 5

Calcugators are experts at setting out short division properly. How about you? Tick the box.

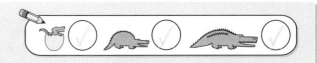

Short Division with Remainders

Mental Maths Warm Up

Answer these as quickly as you can, saying your answer out loud or in your head...

1. Partition 3694 into thousands, hundreds, tens and units.

2. Phil has 43 toy cars which he divides evenly between 4 boxes.
   How many are left over?

3. 5 ÷ 2 = 2 r 1. Write the remainder as a fraction.

4. 617 ÷ 8 leaves a remainder of 1.
   What is the remainder as a fraction?

Answers: 1) 3 thousands, 6 hundreds, 9 tens and 4 units   **2)** 3   **3)** $\frac{1}{2}$ **4)** $\frac{1}{8}$

For each of these questions, write the remainder as a whole number.

One has been done for you.

1   212 ÷ 8

$$8\overline{\smash{)}2\ 1\ ^5 2}\ \ ^{2\ 6}\ r\ 4$$

26 r 4

5   435 ÷ 4

2   875 ÷ 4

6   505 ÷ 9

3   267 ÷ 7

7   5489 ÷ 8

4   386 ÷ 3

8   1247 ÷ 6

Short Division with Remainders

For each of these questions write the remainder as a fraction. One has been done for you.

9 399 ÷ 5

$$\frac{7\ 9}{5\ \lvert\ 3\ 9\ ^49}\ r\ 4\ =79\frac{4}{5}$$

Remember — remainders written as fractions have the number you're dividing by on the bottom.

$$79\frac{4}{5}$$

13 3587 ÷ 4

10 445 ÷ 2

14 7864 ÷ 9

11 658 ÷ 3

15 5050 ÷ 7

12 157 ÷ 6

16 2453 ÷ 8

Calcugators can write remainders in different ways.
What about you? Tick the box.

Long Division with No Remainders

Now try these. Do your working in the spaces, and copy your answers into the boxes.
One has been done for you.

1

```
        1 3
12 | 1 5 6
   - 1 2
       3 6
     - 3 6
         0  ← There's no
               remainder.
```

(2 MARKS)

[13]

3

```
19 | 8 7 4
```

(2 MARKS)

2

```
21 | 6 5 1
```

(2 MARKS)

4

```
32 | 5 4 4
```

(2 MARKS)

Long Division with No Remainders

5

16 | 1 9 0 4

7

29 | 2 4 9 4

6

23 | 6 9 4 6

8

37 | 1 6 6 5

A Calcugator can set out long division like a pro.
Show how you got on by ticking the box.

Long Division with Remainders

Answer these as quickly as you can, saying your answer out loud or in your head...

1. How many lots of 32 are there in 272?

2. What is the remainder of 272 ÷ 32?

3. Rimi has a rope 113 cm long. She cuts as many 20 cm pieces as she can from it. How many 20 cm pieces does she have?

Answers: 1) 8 2) 16 3) 5

Now try these. Do your working in the spaces, and copy your answers into the boxes.
One has been done for you.

1
```
        2 7
  20 | 5 4 2
    -  4 0
       1 4 2
    -  1 4 0
           2
```
(**2** MARKS)

| 27 r 2 |

3

16 | 2 0 1 5

(**2** MARKS)

2

15 | 7 2 6

(**2** MARKS)

4

66 | 6 1 1 6

(**2** MARKS)

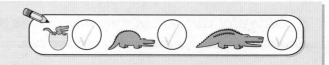

A Calcugator knows how to use long division and end up with remainders. What about you?

Mixed Questions

Mental Maths Warm Up

Answer these as quickly as you can, saying your answer out loud or in your head...

1. Should you do the division or the addition first in this calculation? $6 \div 2 + 7$

2. Should you subtract or multiply first in this calculation? $10 - 4 \times 2$

3. Do these two calculations have the same answer? $(3 \times 2) + 4$ and $3 \times (2 + 4)$

4. Which calculation is right? $5 + 4 \div 2 = 7$ or $(5 + 4) \div 2 = 7$

Answers: 1) division **2)** multiply
3) No (10 and 18) **4)** $5 + 4 \div 2 = 7$

Now try these. Do your working in the spaces, and copy your answers into the boxes.

1 $2 \times 5 + 4$

Don't forget the BODMAS rules.

4 $18 + 18 \div 9$

2 $(6 + 8) \div 2$

5 $99 \div (7 + 4) \times 100$

3 $40 \div (2 \times 2)$

6 $12 - 1 \times 8 + 4$

A Calcugator never muddles up the order of calculations. How did you do with them?

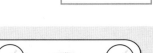

Section 2 — Decimals

Adding Decimals

┌─ Mental Maths Warm Up ─┐

Answer these as quickly as you can, saying your answer out loud or in your head...

1. Think of a number that's bigger than 9 and smaller than 10.
2. What is the value of each digit in the number 0.619?
3. How many decimal places will the answer to 3.2 + 1.75 have?
4. Add 2.5 to 5.3 in your head.

Answers: 1) E.g. 9.5 2) zero units, six tenths, one hundredth, nine thousandths 3) 2 4) 7.8

Now try these. Do your working in the spaces, and copy your answers into the boxes.
One has been done for you.

1 4.2 + 3.4

$$
\begin{array}{r}
4\,.\,2 \\
+\ 3\,.\,4 \\
\hline
7\,.\,6 \\
\end{array}
$$

| 7.6 |

2 11.7 + 23.1

3 6 + 2.5

4 4.64 + 5.35

5 34.6 + 1.1

6 5.71 + 14.23

7 3.3 + 2.64

Make sure you line the decimal points up.

8 1.26 + 12.5

Adding Decimals

 9   1.72 + 6.19

 13   12.91 + 43.24

10   28.38 + 26.45

14   4.67 + 5.85

 11   5.8 + 3.6

15   7.8 + 8.73

Careful lining up the digits with this one.

 12   13.4 + 23.7

16   21.96 + 5.8

Calcugators are really happy adding up decimal numbers in columns. How about you? Tick the box.

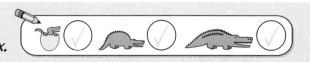

Subtracting Decimals

Now try these. Do your working in the spaces, and copy your answers into the boxes.
One has been done for you.

1   0.9 – 0.3

$$
\begin{array}{r}
0.9 \\
-\ 0.3 \\
\hline
0.6 \\
\end{array}
$$

0.6

2   3.4 – 2.1

3   8.5 – 4

4   12.6 – 7

5   6.78 – 2.15

6   23.8 – 2.6

7   5.69 – 3.4

8   15.75 – 1.5

Subtracting Decimals

9 4.63 – 1.19

13 12.37 – 1.29

10 4.2 – 2.6

14 3.28 – 1.7

11 6.59 – 3.81

15 17.65 – 8.99

12 8.24 – 5.86

16 9 – 6.3

9 is the same as 9.0 — make sure you line the decimal points up before you do the subtraction.

Calcugators eat decimal number subtractions for breakfast. How do you feel about them?

28

Multiplying by 10, 100 and 1000

Mental Maths Warm Up

Answer these as quickly as you can, saying your answer out loud or in your head...

1. Should you multiply 25 by 10, 100 or 1000 to get 250?
2. What should you multiply 7.2 by to get 720?
3. How many numbers will be after the decimal point if you multiply 5.25 by 10?
4. Find the missing number. 12.38 × ? = 12380

Answers: 1) 10 2) 100 3) 1 4) 1000

Now try these ones. Write your answers in the boxes.

1 1.6 × 10

10 has one zero, so move the digits one place to the left.

5 2558.94 × 100

2 2.53 × 10

6 387.684 × 1000

3 723.92 × 100

7 0.4 × 1000

4 7.3 × 100

8 68955.08 × 1000

A fully grown Calcugator can multiply all sorts of decimals by 10, 100 and 1000. How did you do?

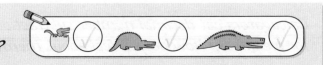

Section 2 — Decimals

© CGP — not to be photocopied

Dividing by 10, 100 and 1000

Mental Maths Warm Up

Answer these as quickly as you can, saying your answer out loud or in your head...

1. Should you divide 1.5 by 10, 100 or 1000 to get 0.015?
2. Work out the missing number. 6.3 ÷ ? = 0.63
3. How many numbers will be after the decimal point if you divide 20.9 by 100?
4. What should you divide 134 by to get 0.134?

Answers: 1) 100 2) 10 3) 3 4) 1000

Now try these ones. Write your answers in the boxes.

1   1.3 ÷ 10

5   0.7 ÷ 100

2   128.67 ÷ 10

6   5346 ÷ 1000

3   1856 ÷ 100

7   193 ÷ 1000

4   93907 ÷ 100

8   12 ÷ 1000

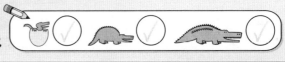

A Calcugator is happy dividing by 10, 100 and 1000 to get decimal answers. How about you? Tick the box.

Multiplying with Decimals

Answer these as quickly as you can, saying your answer out loud or in your head...

1. What is two lots of 0.5?
2. $15 \times 4 = 60$. What's 1.5×4?
3. Ailsa is working out 2.3×9, which whole numbers can she multiply to help her?
4. Is the answer to 0.7×8 more or less than 56?

Answers: 1) 1 **2)** 6 **3)** E.g. 23×9 **4)** less

Now try these. Do your working in the spaces, and copy your answers into the boxes.
Write your answers as decimals where necessary. One has been done for you.

1 0.7×3

$$7 \times 3 = 21$$
$$21 \div 10 = 2.1$$

> 2.1

5 2.1×6

2 0.4×5

6 5.8×7

3 1.2×4

7 0.9×37

4 0.3×11

8 0.6×123

Multiplying with Decimals

9 0.12 × 2

13 1.34 × 4

10 0.22 × 3

14 8.13 × 9

11 0.73 × 7

15 46.37 × 6

12 2.13 × 3

16 16.59 × 8

Calcugators can multiply numbers with up to two decimal places by a whole number. How about you?

Dividing with Decimals

Mental Maths Warm Up

Answer these as quickly as you can, saying your answer out loud or in your head...

1. Estimate the answer to $51 \div 5$.

2. What's $\frac{1}{2}$ as a decimal?

3. Find the missing number in this calculation. $\frac{3}{4} = ? \times \frac{1}{4}$

4. Given that $\frac{1}{5}$ as a decimal is 0.2, what is $\frac{3}{5}$ as a decimal?

Answers: 1) 10 2) 0.5 3) 3 4) 0.6

Now try these. Do your working in the spaces, and copy your answers into the boxes.
Give your answers as decimals. One has been done for you.

1 $3 \div 2$

$3 \div 2 = 1$ remainder 1

$= 1\frac{1}{2}$

$= 1.5$

1.5

5 $21 \div 6$

2 $6 \div 4$

6 $50 \div 8$

3 $9 \div 4$

7 $62 \div 5$

4 $36 \div 5$

8 $92 \div 8$

A Calcugator can use times tables and fractions to
do divisions with decimal answers. How about you?

Short and Long Division with Decimals

Mental Maths Warm Up

Answer these as quickly as you can, saying your answer out loud or in your head...

1. How many lots of 12 are there in 48?

2. What's the remainder when you divide 51 by 12?

3. How many tens is six hundreds?

4. How many tenths is four units?

Answers: 1) 4 2) 3 3) 60 4) 40

Now try these. Give your answers as decimals in the boxes. One has been done for you.

1   152 ÷ 5

$$5\overline{)1\;5\;2\;.^2O}$$
$$3\;O\;.\;4$$

30.4

2   89 ÷ 5

3   129 ÷ 6

4   196 ÷ 8

5   1026 ÷ 4

6   631 ÷ 5

7   393 ÷ 5

8   258 ÷ 8

Short and Long Division with Decimals

Use long division for these. Give your answers as decimals. One has been done for you.

9

```
        1 3 . 5
  34 | 4 5 9 . 0
     - 3 4
       1 1 9
     - 1 0 2
         1 7 0
       - 1 7 0
             0
```

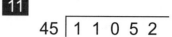

13.5

11

```
  45 | 1 1 0 5 2
```

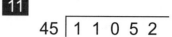

10

```
  22 | 2 8 9 3
```

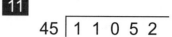

12

```
  8 | 9 6 5 4
```

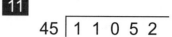

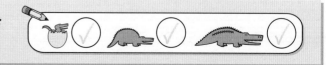

A fully grown Calcugator can find decimal answers using long and short division. How did you do?

Adding Fractions

Mental Maths Warm Up

Answer these as quickly as you can, saying your answer out loud or in your head...

1. How many quarters are there in six wholes?

2. Hani ate half of his birthday cake in the morning and another quarter in the afternoon. How much of the cake did he eat altogether?

3. What is $\frac{1}{3} + \frac{1}{3} + \frac{1}{3} + \frac{1}{3}$?

Answers: 1) 24 **2)** three quarters **3)** $\frac{4}{3}$ or $1\frac{1}{3}$

Now try these. Do your working in the spaces, and copy your answers into the boxes.
One has been done for you.

1 $\frac{1}{7} + \frac{4}{7}$

$$\frac{1}{7} + \frac{4}{7} = \frac{1+4}{7} = \frac{5}{7}$$ $\boxed{\dfrac{5}{7}}$

2 $\frac{2}{5} + \frac{2}{5}$

3 $\frac{2}{9} + \frac{3}{9}$

4 $\frac{3}{8} + \frac{4}{8}$

5 $\frac{1}{11} + \frac{5}{11}$

6 $\frac{7}{12} + \frac{4}{12}$

7 $\frac{10}{15} + \frac{3}{15}$

8 $\frac{6}{17} + \frac{11}{17}$

A fully grown Calcugator is happy adding fractions with the same denominator. How did you get on?

Adding Fractions with Different Denominators

Mental Maths Warm Up

Answer these as quickly as you can, saying your answer out loud or in your head...

1. How many times does 4 go into 20?
2. What's $\frac{1}{2}$ written with a denominator of 8?
3. What do you have to do to $\frac{1}{3}$ so you can add it to $\frac{1}{6}$?
4. What's the smallest number that both 6 and 10 go into?

Answers: 1) 5 2) $\frac{4}{8}$
3) multiply the top and bottom by 2
4) 30

Now try these. Give your answers in their simplest form. Do your working in the spaces, and copy your answers into the boxes. One has been done for you.

1 $\frac{1}{2} + \frac{1}{4}$

$$\frac{1}{2} = \frac{1 \times 2}{2 \times 2} = \frac{2}{4}$$

$$\frac{2}{4} + \frac{1}{4} = \frac{2+1}{4} = \frac{3}{4}$$

$\frac{3}{4}$

5 $\frac{3}{5} + \frac{1}{20}$

2 $\frac{1}{3} + \frac{1}{9}$

6 $\frac{4}{7} + \frac{3}{14}$

3 $\frac{1}{4} + \frac{3}{8}$

7 $\frac{5}{9} + \frac{5}{27}$

4 $\frac{2}{3} + \frac{1}{6}$

8 $\frac{5}{24} + \frac{3}{4}$

Adding Fractions with Different Denominators

Try these. Give your answers in their simplest form. One has been done for you.

9 $\frac{1}{3} + \frac{1}{4}$ 12 is a common multiple of 3 and 4

$\frac{1}{3} = \frac{1 \times 4}{3 \times 4} = \frac{4}{12}$ $\frac{1}{4} = \frac{1 \times 3}{4 \times 3} = \frac{3}{12}$

$\frac{4}{12} + \frac{3}{12} = \frac{4 + 3}{12} = \frac{7}{12}$ $\boxed{\dfrac{7}{12}}$

10 $\frac{1}{7} + \frac{1}{9}$

11 $\frac{2}{3} + \frac{1}{5}$

12 $\frac{5}{9} + \frac{5}{12}$

13 $\frac{1}{6} + \frac{3}{8}$

14 $\frac{4}{15} + \frac{1}{20}$

15 $\frac{4}{21} + \frac{3}{14}$

16 $\frac{9}{24} + \frac{3}{16}$ *Don't forget to simplify your answer.*

Different denominators are no match for Calcugators. But are you up to the challenge? Tick the box.

Subtracting Fractions

Now try these. Give your answers in their simplest form. Do your working in the spaces, and copy your answers into the boxes. One has been done for you.

1 $\frac{5}{6} - \frac{4}{6}$

$$\frac{5}{6} - \frac{4}{6} = \frac{5-4}{6} = \frac{1}{6}$$

$\boxed{\dfrac{1}{6}}$

5 $\frac{5}{6} - \frac{2}{6}$

$\boxed{}$

2 $\frac{4}{5} - \frac{2}{5}$

$\boxed{}$

6 $\frac{13}{15} - \frac{8}{15}$

$\boxed{}$

3 $\frac{8}{14} - \frac{3}{14}$

$\boxed{}$

7 $\frac{11}{12} - \frac{3}{12}$

$\boxed{}$

4 $\frac{3}{4} - \frac{1}{4}$

Don't forget to simplify your answer.

$\boxed{}$

8 $\frac{4}{7} - \frac{6}{7}$

You should get a negative fraction as your answer for this one.

$\boxed{}$

Calcugators can subtract fractions in a snap. Tick the box to show how you did with them.

Subtracting Fractions with Different Denominators

Mental Maths Warm Up

Answer these as quickly as you can, saying your answer out loud or in your head...

1. What should you divide the top and bottom of $\frac{5}{15}$ by to get it in its simplest form?
2. Find the number that's missing in this pair of equivalent fractions: $\frac{1}{3} = \frac{?}{18}$
3. What do you have to do to $\frac{2}{5}$ so you can take it away from $\frac{7}{10}$?
4. What's the smallest number that 8 and 5 both go into?

Answers: 1) 5 2) 6 3) multiply top and bottom by 2 4) 40

Now try these. Put each answer in the box in its simplest form. One has been done for you.

1 $\frac{7}{8} - \frac{1}{4}$

$$\frac{1}{4} = \frac{1 \times 2}{4 \times 2} = \frac{2}{8}$$

$$\frac{7}{8} - \frac{2}{8} = \frac{7-2}{8} = \frac{5}{8}$$

$$\boxed{\frac{5}{8}}$$

4 $\frac{7}{8} - \frac{2}{3}$

2 $\frac{3}{5} - \frac{7}{15}$

5 $\frac{6}{9} - \frac{3}{10}$

Don't forget to simplify your answer.

3 $\frac{3}{5} - \frac{1}{2}$

6 $\frac{7}{18} - \frac{5}{6}$

*Calcugators aren't put off by different denominators.
How about you? Tick the box to show how you did.*

Mixed Numbers

Now try these. Answer with mixed numbers in their simplest form. One has been done for you.

1 $\quad 4\frac{4}{7} + \frac{2}{7}$

$$4\frac{4}{7} + \frac{2}{7} = 4 + \frac{4}{7} + \frac{2}{7}$$

$$= 4 + \frac{6}{7} = 4\frac{6}{7}$$

$$\boxed{4\frac{6}{7}}$$

4 $\quad 8\frac{13}{15} - \frac{2}{5}$

2 $\quad \frac{2}{5} + 7\frac{1}{5}$

5 $\quad \frac{5}{12} + 2\frac{1}{4}$

3 $\quad 6\frac{1}{4} + \frac{1}{2}$

6 $\quad 3\frac{5}{8} - \frac{4}{16}$

Mixed Numbers

Now have a go at these. Give your answers as mixed numbers in their simplest form.

Do your working in the spaces, and put your answers in the boxes. One has been done for you.

7 $1\frac{2}{3} + \frac{5}{6}$

$1\frac{2}{3} = \frac{(1 \times 3) + 2}{3} = \frac{5}{3} = \frac{10}{6}$

$\frac{10}{6} + \frac{5}{6} = \frac{15}{6} = \frac{5}{2}$

$\frac{5}{2} = \frac{2+2+1}{2}$

$\quad = \frac{2}{2} + \frac{2}{2} + \frac{1}{2} = 2\frac{1}{2}$

$\boxed{2\frac{1}{2}}$

8 $2\frac{7}{15} + 1\frac{2}{5}$

9 $2\frac{1}{8} - \frac{3}{4}$

10 $2\frac{7}{9} + 1\frac{2}{5}$

For these you need to find a number that both denominators go into.

11 $4\frac{1}{6} - 2\frac{11}{18}$

12 $1\frac{5}{7} - 2\frac{1}{4}$

Mixed numbers don't bother Calcugators — they're happy to add and subtract them. How about you?

Multiplying Fractions

Answer these as quickly as you can, saying your answer out loud or in your head...

1. Work out the missing number in this multiplication. $\frac{2}{3} \times \frac{5}{7} = \frac{2 \times ?}{3 \times 7} = \frac{10}{21}$

2. Find the missing number. $\frac{3}{4} \times 2 = 2 \times ? \div 4$

3. Write $4\frac{3}{8}$ as a sum of a whole number and a fraction.

4. $4 \times 2 = 8$ and $\frac{3}{8} \times 2 = \frac{3}{4}$. What is $4\frac{3}{8} \times 2$?

Answers: 1) 5 2) 3 3) 4 + $\frac{3}{8}$ 4) $8\frac{3}{4}$

Now try these. Give your answers in their simplest form. Do your working in the spaces, and copy your answers into the boxes. The first one has been done for you.

1 $\frac{1}{3} \times \frac{1}{6}$

$$\frac{1}{3} \times \frac{1}{6} = \frac{1 \times 1}{3 \times 6} = \frac{1}{18}$$

$\boxed{\dfrac{1}{18}}$

5 $\frac{8}{9} \times \frac{7}{10}$

2 $\frac{7}{9} \times \frac{4}{5}$

6 $\frac{12}{20} \times \frac{3}{8}$

3 $\frac{5}{6} \times \frac{7}{8}$

7 $\frac{6}{14} \times \frac{10}{12}$

4 $\frac{3}{11} \times \frac{6}{8}$

8 $\frac{6}{25} \times \frac{15}{16}$

Multiplying Fractions

For these, give your answers as mixed numbers in their simplest form.

The first one has been done for you.

9 $\frac{1}{2} \times 5$

$5 \times 1 = 5$

$5 \div 2 = 2\frac{1}{2}$

$2\frac{1}{2}$

10 $\frac{3}{7} \times 9$

11 $1\frac{5}{8} \times 3$

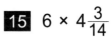

Multiply the whole number and the fraction separately, then add them together.

12 $3\frac{5}{6} \times 4$

13 $7 \times 2\frac{4}{11}$

14 $7\frac{8}{15} \times 3$

15 $6 \times 4\frac{3}{14}$

16 $5\frac{3}{4} \times 8$

Fully grown Calcugators like nothing better than multiplying fractions. How do you feel?

Dividing Fractions

Mental Maths Warm Up

Answer these as quickly as you can, saying your answer out loud or in your head...

1. Arthur divides half a custard tart into two equal pieces.
   What fraction of the whole custard tart is each piece?

2. Work out the missing number in this calculation: $\frac{1}{5} \div 2 = \frac{1}{5 \times ?} = \frac{1}{10}$

3. $\frac{1}{3} \div 5 = \frac{1}{15}$. What's $\frac{2}{3} \div 5$?

Answers: 1) $\frac{1}{4}$ 2) 2 3) $\frac{2}{15}$

Now try these. Give your answers in their simplest form. Do your working in the spaces, and copy your answers into the boxes. The first one has been done for you.

1 $\frac{1}{4} \div 3$

$$\frac{1}{4} \div 3 = \frac{1}{4 \times 3} = \frac{1}{12}$$

$$\boxed{\frac{1}{12}}$$

5 $\frac{2}{3} \div 12$

2 $\frac{3}{5} \div 4$

6 $\frac{10}{11} \div 35$

3 $\frac{7}{8} \div 5$

7 $\frac{6}{8} \div 14$

4 $\frac{5}{12} \div 4$

8 $\frac{6}{7} \div 19$

Calcugators are really quite good at dividing fractions by whole numbers. How about you? Tick the box.

Percentages

┌─ Mental Maths Warm Up ───┐

Answer these as quickly as you can, saying your answer out loud or in your head...

1. Find the missing number. $57\% = \frac{?}{100}$

2. What is $\frac{20}{100}$ in its simplest form?

3. Kirstie is working out 20% of 50. She has written the calculation $\frac{1}{5} \times ?$
   What is the missing number in her calculation?

Answers: 1) 57 2) $\frac{1}{5}$ 3) 50

└──┘

Now try these. Do your working in the spaces, and copy your answers into the boxes.
One has been done for you.

1 50% of 12

$50\% = \frac{50}{100} = \frac{1}{2}$

$\frac{1}{2} \times 12 = \frac{12}{2} = 6$

> 6

2 20% of 25

3 30% of 40

4 80% of 65

5 60% of 150

6 70% of 210

7 40% of 7

You should get a decimal answer for this one.

8 90% of 53

Percentages

Have a go at these. Do your working in the spaces. One has been done for you.

9 25% of 16

$$25\% = \frac{25}{100} = \frac{1}{4}$$

$$\frac{1}{4} \times 16 = \frac{16}{4} = 4$$

4

10 75% of 24

11 15% of 80

12 65% of 60

13 70% of 420

14 30% of 320

15 18% of 50

16 22% of 150

A fully grown Calcugator would have no trouble finding percentages like these ones. How did you get on?